grade
5

For full details of exam requirements, please refer to the current syllabus in conjunction with *Examination Information & Regulations* and the guide for candidates, teachers and parents, *These Music Exams*. These three documents are available online at www.abrsm.org, as well as free of charge from music retailers, from ABRSM local representatives or from the Services Department, The Associated Board of the Royal Schools of Music, 24 Portland Place, London W1B 1LU, United Kingdom.

CONTENTS

In this album, editorial additions to the texts are given in small print, within square brackets, or – in the case of slurs and ties – in the form ⌢. Metronome marks, breath marks (retained here where they appear in the source edition) and ornament realizations (suggested for exam purposes) are for guidance only; they are not comprehensive or obligatory.

Footnotes: Anthony Burton

DO NOT PHOTOCOPY © MUSIC

Alternative pieces for this grade

© 2007 by The Associated Board of the Royal Schools of Music

No part of this publication may be copied or reproduced in any form or by any means without the prior permission of the publisher.

Music origination by Barnes Music Engraving Ltd
Cover by Økvik Design
Printed in England by Halstan & Co. Ltd, Amersham, Bucks.

Largo and Allemanda

First and second movements from Sonata in G minor,
Op. 5 (Book 1) No. 6

Edited and continuo realization by
Paul Everett

J. B. LOEILLET

Jean Baptiste Loeillet (1688–c.1720) called himself in print 'Loeillet de Gant', or 'Loeillet of Ghent', presumably to distinguish himself from another member of his Flemish musical family with the same name. His first four sets of solo sonatas are for recorder and keyboard, but the last, published in 1717, specifies the transverse flute (with oboe or violin as alternatives). The sixth sonata of this set begins with a slow movement (but not too slow) and a lively movement in the dance rhythm of the Allemanda. The only dynamics in the original are the indications of echo effects towards the end of the Allemanda; others, within square brackets, are suggestions for exam purposes and may be varied. All breathing or phrasing commas (ϑ) are editorial suggestions.

Allemanda

Vivace [♩ = c.100]

Allegro ma non troppo

Third movement from Sonata in F

Edited and continuo realization by
Hugo Ruf

ANNA AMALIA, PRINCESS OF PRUSSIA

Anna Amalia, Princess of Prussia (1723–87), was a proficient keyboard player and studied composition with a pupil of J. S. Bach. One of her surviving works is a sonata for flute and keyboard, dated 1771 and no doubt intended for her flute-playing brother, the Emperor Frederick the Great. Its finale is in the typically ornate style of the time, which means that the cautionary tempo marking of *Allegro ma non troppo* ('fast, but not too fast') should be heeded. The dynamics are suggestions for exam purposes and may be varied.

A:3

Largo and Allegro

Third and fourth movements from Sonata in B minor, HWV 376

Edited by Terence Best;
continuo realization by Max Schneider

attrib. HANDEL

This sonata was published in London in 1730 as by George Frideric Handel (1685–1759), but that may have been to boost sales of the set in which it was included. The editor of this edition, Terence Best, considers that this and another 'Handel' sonata in the same set 'may just conceivably be early works, but no other source for them exists, and they are most probably spurious'. These last two movements should be played without a long break after the cadence of the Largo. Both are in triple time: watch out for 'hemiola' patterns of one big 3/2 bar across two bars of 3/4, or of 3/4 across two bars of 3/8. Several cadences in both movements would benefit from trills on the preceding dotted note, usually starting on a long upper note on the beat; some other ornamentation could be added in places. The dynamics are suggestions for exam purposes and may be varied.

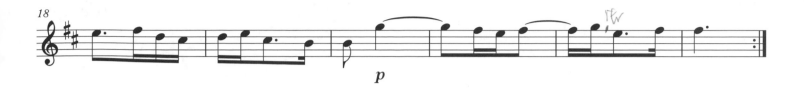

Circus-Pony

STEPHEN DODGSON

The English composer Stephen Dodgson (b. 1924) is probably best known for his guitar music, though he has written for many different instruments. This piece, from an album published in 1978, needs light, precise articulation to create the effect of a prancing pony as suggested by the title.

B:2

March of the Fool

No. 6 from *Portraits*

JOHN McCABE

26 Jan

Moderato ♩ = up to 120

John McCabe (b. 1939) is well known in his native Britain and abroad as a composer and pianist; his works include three major ballet scores, six symphonies, numerous concertos, and many smaller pieces. This March, from a suite written in 1980, is what is sometimes called a 'patrol', beginning as if in the distance, coming closer, then receding again. The composer has written: 'This piece is simply a very gradual *cresc.* to *ff* and then a slow *dim.* The dynamics in brackets indicate the progress of the *cresc.* and the *dim.*' He explains that the piece is so-called because it 'contains a brief reference to the Ballet Music from Holst's opera *The Perfect Fool*'.

AB 3343

Prelude

No. 6 from *Six Preludes*, Op. 23

B:3

Arranged by
Ian Denley

L. BERKELEY

Sir Lennox Berkeley (1903–89) was one of the most respected British composers of his generation, and his music for his own instrument, the piano, is especially admired. His *Six Preludes* for piano of 1945 were commissioned by the BBC to be played, from a recording, to fill gaps left by under-running live radio programmes. The last Prelude, here arranged for flute and piano, is in the dance rhythm of the siciliana.

C:2

Pieces I and II

from *Acht Stücke für Flöte allein*

HINDEMITH

I

As well as writing operas and large-scale orchestral works, the German composer Paul Hindemith (1895–1963) produced a large amount of music suitable for students or amateurs – known as 'Gebrauchsmusik' or 'music for use'. The first of these *Eight Pieces for Solo Flute* from 1927 needs precise definition of its different rhythms. The second has no regular pulse: the bars are of varying lengths, and there are repeated notes in free time. You might like to think of it as an instrumental equivalent of birdsong.

II

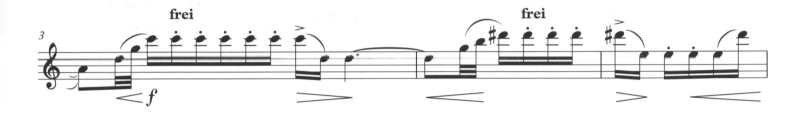

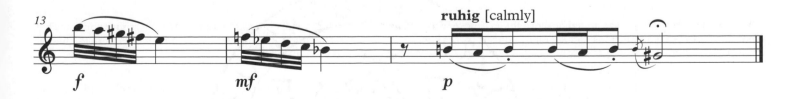

C:3

Study in C
No. 1 from *15 Easy Studies*, Op. 33 Book 1

Edited by
Edward Blakeman

E. KÖHLER

Ernesto Köhler (1849–1907) was an Italian-born flute virtuoso who held important orchestral positions in Vienna and St Petersburg and travelled around Europe. His compositions include many concert pieces and studies for flute. This study, in a somewhat operatic style, is from the first of three books of studies that comprise a tutor called *Progress in Flute Playing*, published in about 1888.

C:1

Boiling Point

from *Flute Salad*

OLIVER LEDBURY

Latin feel: quick and playful [♩ = c.84]

This piece, by the film and television composer Oliver Ledbury, is from a collection of 'unaccompanied solos for flute in a variety of styles' which was published in 1994. The 'Latin feel' comes from the syncopated groupings of quavers within the 2/2 bars – usually but not always 3+3+2.

Reproduced by permission. All rights reserved. International Copyright Secured. All enquiries for this piece, apart from those directly relating to the exams, should be addressed to Brass Wind Publications, 4 St Mary's Road, Manton, Oakham, Rutland, LE15 8SU.